Buzz off!

Story by Gordon Green

Illustrations by Sholto Walker

The fly flies high in the sky
whizzing to and fro.
Darting, swooping,
loop the **looping**,
always on the go.

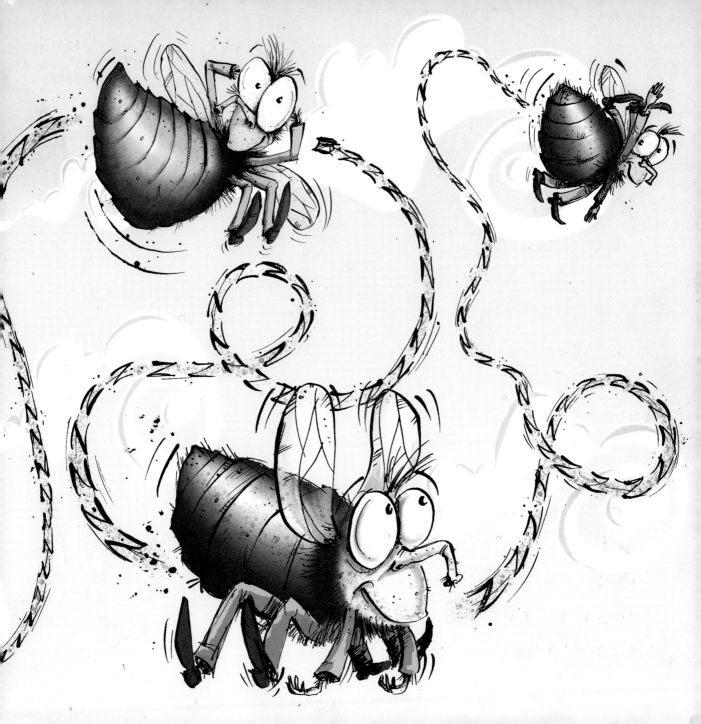

BZZZZZZZZZZZZZZZZZ
ZZZZZZ

As the sun begins to set
the day comes to a close.
The fly must try and find a spot
to rest and have a doze!

"I'm so weary," says the fly.
"I need to just chill out."
He sees pig wallowing in the mud,
and perches on his snout.

"Oink!" says pig with a great big snort
and blows poor fly away.
"Buzz off!" he says "You can't rest here!
Find somewhere else to stay."

"You look tired" the spider says,
"I have the perfect bed.
It's cosy, soft and very springy,
come rest upon my web."

"I'll pass if you don't mind" says fly.
"I know your crafty game.
I think I'll search around some more,
but thank you all the same."

"Boy I'm **whacked**" yawns the fly.
"I need to find a bed."
He sees horse grazing in the meadow,
and lands upon his head.

"Neigh!" says horse and shakes his head and flicks poor fly away.
"Buzz off!" he says "You can't stop here! Find somewhere else to stay."

"If you need a friend" frog says,
"you're luck has just begun.
I have the perfect bed for you,
come lie upon my tongue."

"I'll pass if you don't mind" says fly.
"I know **your** crafty game.
I think I'll search around some more,
but thank you all the same."

"Boy I'm *pooped*" says the fly.
"I need to get some sleep."
He spies a *comfy* woolly bed,
and comes to rest on sheep.

"Baa!" says sheep and shakes his coat
and tumbles fly away.
"Buzz off!" he says "You can't stop here!
Find somewhere else to stay!"

"Howdy Fly" the magpie says,
"you look tired and weak.
Stop and take a moment out,
come nap upon my beak."

"I'll pass if you don't mind" says fly.
"I know your crafty game.
I think I'll search around some more,
but thank you all the same."

"Gosh I'm tired" says the fly.
"I need to find repose."
He sees cow chomping on some grass,
and lands upon her nose.

"Moo" says cow and gives a snort
and shoos poor fly away.
"Buzz off!" she says "You can't stop here!
Find somewhere else to stay!"

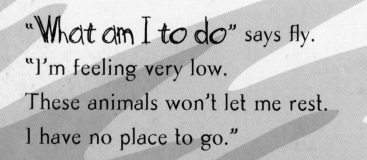

"What am I to do" says fly.
"I'm feeling very low.
These animals won't let me rest.
I have no place to go."

"No need to worry" says the cow.
"I've the perfect bed for you.
It's warm and soft and freshly made,
my steaming fresh...cow poo!!

Fly took up cow's kind offer,
so this is how it ends.
He finally had a resting place,
and also made some friends.